Contents

KT-376-436

KNOWSLEY LIBRARY SERVICE

270610013

Bertrams 604560

18/9/09 HALEWOOD

Characters

The Arkies

Singer

Gentle Singer can sense the mind of any living being, and communicate by thought alone. She understands many languages.

Lyam

Science whiz Lyam can tell the Arkies everything they need to know about alien plant and animal life – and then some.

Merlinna

Merlinna is always ready for a battle. She's an expert with weapons – including her naturally piercing screech.

Pace

Pace is a practical guy with a very practical skill – he can communicate with electronic equipment. He and Singer are special friends.

EarthNet

Tench and Farla are EarthNet agents who trail the *Ark3*. They want to capture the Arkies and return them to Earth.

Tench

Farla

PLANET OF BONES

by Sally Odgers

illustrated by Georgina Thomas

SCHOLASTIC

THE ARKIES

All rights reserved.
This 2009 edition published in the United Kingdom by
Scholastic Ltd
Villiers House
Clarendon Avenue
Leamington Spa
Warwickshire
CV32 5PR

First published in 2007
by Macmillan Education Australia Pty Ltd.

Copyright © 2007 Laguna Bay Publishing Pty Ltd.
www.lagunabaypublishing.com

All rights reserved.

Text by Sally Odgers
Illustrations by Georgina Thomas
Cover Design Allison Parry
Design by Matt Lin/Goblin Design
Managing Editor Nicola Robinson

No Part of this publication may be reproduced, stored in a retrieval system, or transmitted, in any form or by any means, electronic, mechanical, photocopying, recording or otherwise, without the prior permission of the publisher. This book remains in copyright, although permission is granted to copy pages where indicated for classroom distribution and use only in the school which has purchased the book, or by the teacher who has purchased the book, and in accordance with the CLA licensing agreement. Photocopying permission is given only for purchasers and not for borrowers of books from any lending service.

Out of this World: Planet of Bones
ISBN 978 1407 10112 5

Printed by Tien Wah Press, Singapore

1 2 3 4 5 6 7 8 9   9 0 1 2 3 4 5 6 7 8

THE SPACESHIP ARK3 IS IN ORBIT AROUND A PLANET. ON BOARD ARE THE ARKIES, FOUR TEENAGE FRIENDS WHO ARE SEARCHING FOR NEW SETTLEMENT-READY (S-R) PLANETS. EVERY DAY BRINGS A NEW ADVENTURE ...

PACE ENLISTS THE HELP OF THE SHIP'S COMPUTER, ARKMA.
REPORT, ARKMA! WHAT'S IT LIKE DOWN THERE?

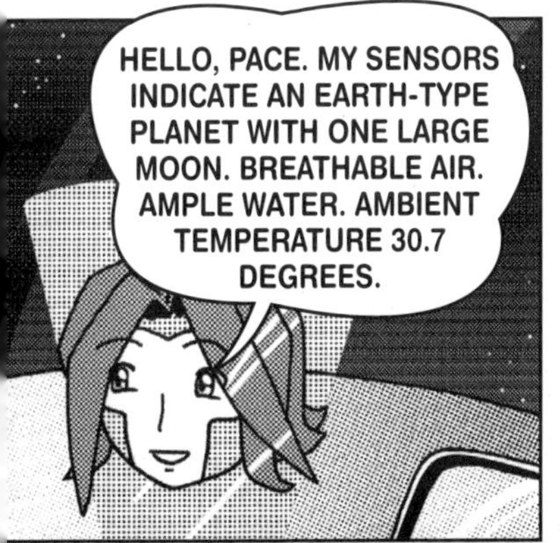
HELLO, PACE. MY SENSORS INDICATE AN EARTH-TYPE PLANET WITH ONE LARGE MOON. BREATHABLE AIR. AMPLE WATER. AMBIENT TEMPERATURE 30.7 DEGREES.

SOUNDING GOOD!

ANOTHER SPACESHIP APPEARS.

IT FOLLOWS ARK3 TOWARDS THE NEW PLANET.

SUDDENLY, THE ARKIES ARE HAILED BY A VOICE THEY KNOW ALL TOO WELL.
ARK3! THIS IS FARLA FETTLEMAN OF EARTHNET 9. DO NOT LAND ON THAT PLANET.
DON'T THOSE EARTHNET AGENTS EVER GIVE UP? SINGER, DO YOU SENSE ANY DIDGIES?
Ark3

NOT SO FAR.

TURN THE RECEIVER OFF, MERLINNA. ARKMA! TAKE US DOWN.

INITIATING LANDIN
SEQUENCE. WILL LAN
IN TEN MINUTES.

THE EARTHNET AGENTS TRY TO THWART THE ARKIES' PLANS.
REPEAT! DO NOT LAND ON THAT PLANET!
DON'T WASTE YOUR BREATH, FARLA. DO YOU WANT TO GO AFTER THEM?

IGNORING THIS ...

... ARK3 DESCENDS RAPIDLY TO THE PLANET'S SURFACE.

SHHHOOOOO!

PREPARE FOR LANDING! 10, 9, 8, 7, 6, 5, 4, 3, 2, 1 ... DOWN!

SSSSSHHHHH!

ONCE ARK3 IS SECURED THE ARKIES GO OUT TO DO SOME EXPLORING.
MAYBE THIS PLANET WILL BE ONE WE CAN RECOMMEND FOR SETTLEMENT.
I DO HOPE SO. IT'S BEEN SUCH A LONG TIME.

WILL YOU LOOK AT THAT!
WOW! BONES!
GASP!
GLAD I HAVE MY TANGLE-LINE.
Ark3

OH-OH. THIS DOESN'T LOOK GOOD.
WHAT COULD HAVE KILLED THESE?
LET'S HOPE IT ISN'T STILL HERE.
THESE BONES ARE GREAT! I'LL HAVE TO RUN SOME TESTS RIGHT AWAY. COME ON PACE, USE THE MATCON TO BUILD A SHELTER.
ONE SHELTER COMING UP, LYAM.
I'M GOING MONSTER HUNTING. WANT TO COME, SINGER?
NO THANKS. I'M ALMOST SURE THERE'S NOTHING ALIVE AROUND HERE.

MATCON IN HAND, PACE SEARCHES FOR THE PERFECT ROCK.
THIS ONE LOOKS GOOD.
IT WILL DO. C'MON, LITTLE BRO, LET'S TURN THIS ROCK INTO A SHELTER.
PACE AIMS THE MATCON AT THE ROCK. IT CAN CONVERT MATTER TO JUST ABOUT ANYTHING.
ZZZZZZZZZ
LOOKING GOOD, PACE.

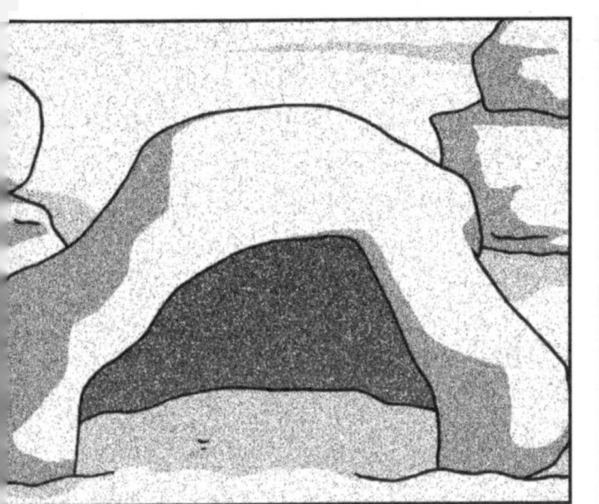

I NEED TO TEST THESE BONES FOR SIGNS OF TRAUMA OR DISEASE.
THERE ARE WAY TOO MANY OF THEM TO BE THE RESULT OF DEATH BY NATURAL CAUSES.

VELCOME TO YOUR NEW LABORATORY, MISTER ZIENTIST!

ZANK YOU, ZANK YOU.

DID YOU SEE ANYTHING, MERLINNA?

ALL CLEAR.

HEY LYAM, I THOUGHT YOU MIGHT LIKE MORE BONES TO STUDY.

SOON LYAM IS BUSY TESTING BONES. THE ARKIES CAN'T RECOMMEND THIS PLANET FOR SETTLEMENT IF IT'S DANGEROUS. THEY ARE ALL SO BUSY THEY DON'T NOTICE THE MOONRISE.
Ark3

IT'S AS IF THESE CREATURES JUST LAY DOWN AND DIED.

Ark3

WHAT'S THAT NOISE?
IT'S A KIND OF RUMBLING. IT'S ... NO!
RUMRUM

ARE WE UNDER SOME KIND OF ATTACK?
ARGHHHHHH! LOOK!
NO! I DON'T BELIEVE THIS!
THE MOON! THE – ARGHHHHH!

CRASH!
GRROWL!

TSUNAMI!

SSSSSHHHHH!

WE HAVE TO GET BACK TO ARK3!
RUN!

S THE ARKIES RUN FOR THEIR LIVES, THE WALL OF WATER RACES
FTER THEM. JUST BEFORE IT BREAKS, PACE HAS AN IDEA.
GRROWL!

IT INVOLVES MERLINNA'S WEAPON, THE TANGLE-LINE!
QUICK, MERLINNA. GIVE ME YOUR TANGLE-LINE.
WE'RE GOING TO BE DROWNED AND YOU WANT TO BORROW MY TANGLE-LINE?

JUST GIVE IT TO ME.
I CAN USE THE MATCON TO CONVERT THE TANGLE-LINE.

HERE!
OK! BE READY TO GRAB ON TIGHT.

EVERYONE, BEHIND THESE ROCKS!

QUICK MERLINNA, EXTEND YOUR TANGLE-LINE ALL THE WAY OUT.

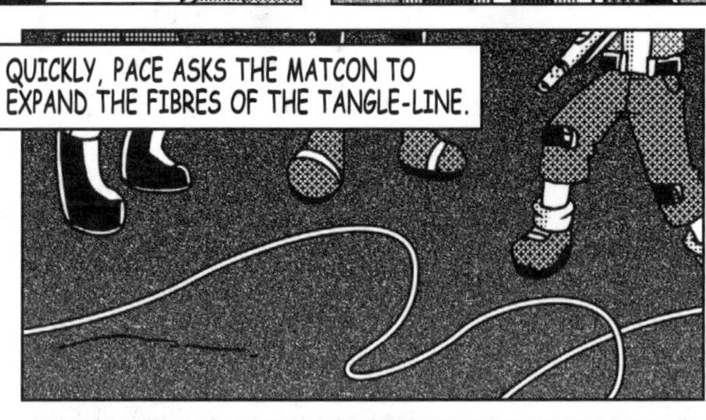
QUICKLY, PACE ASKS THE MATCON TO EXPAND THE FIBRES OF THE TANGLE-LINE.

C'MON, LITTLE BRO! DON'T LET ME DOWN NOW.

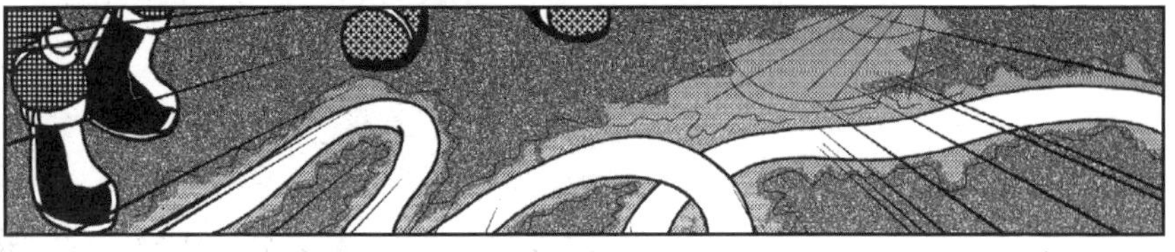

HURRY, PACE! THE WAVE IS ALMOST UPON US! QUICK!!
GRAB ON, EVERYONE. WE'RE GOING FOR A RIDE.
GUESS WE NOW KNOW WHY THERE'S SO MANY BONES HERE.
WE'LL BE BONES IF THIS DOESN'T WORK.
CRASH!
HERE WE GO!

THE ARKIES STRUGGLE TO STAY AFLOAT.
HOLD ON EVERYBODY! TIGHT!
ARGHHH!

THE GREAT WAVE HITS!
SMASH!

PACE? AMBIENT TEMPERATURE FALLING. HUMIDITY RISING. STATUS INOPERABLE. CLOSING DOWNNNNNN.

GUYS? GUYS?
WHERE ARE YOU?

I'M HERE,
PACE. ARE
YOU OK?
YES. LOOKS LIKE
WE'RE ALL HERE.

BUT WHAT
ABOUT ARK3?

OUR SHIP'S
GONE!

LOOK AT THE SIZE
OF THAT MOON!

IT'S SO HUGE! I BET THAT'S WHAT CAUSED THAT WAVE ...
I THOUGHT UNDERWATER EARTHQUAKES CAUSED TSUNAMIS?

THEY DO, BUT THIS ISN'T A TSUNAMI. I BELIEVE THIS IS A NATURAL TIDE, CAUSED BY THAT GIANT MOON.

IF THIS TIDE HAPPENS REGULARLY, HOW COULD ANYTHING LIVE HERE?
PERHAPS NOTHING DOES.

ANOTHER WAVE CARRIES THE ARKIES UP AND AWAY, BUT LYAM CONTINUES TO EXPLAIN HIS THEORY.
PERHAPS THAT MOON HAS BEEN CAPTURED RECENTLY IN THE PLANET'S HISTORY.
HERE WE GO AGAIN!
THEN IT WOULD HAVE CAUSED TERRIBLE UPHEAVALS.
FLOOD TIDES. LIKE THIS.
SSSSSSHHHHHH!

AS THE ARKIES FLOAT ONWARDS, THE SUN COMES UP. BUT THE HUGE MOON STILL DOMINATES THE SKY.
PERHAPS WE SHOULD HAVE LISTENED TO FARLA'S WARNING AFTER ALL.
AT LAST THEY DRIFT TOWARDS AN ISLAND.
LOOK! LET'S TRY TO GET TO IT. EVERYBODY KICK AS HARD AS YOU CAN!
SPLASH!

chapter 3 : Safe?

HE CONVINCES THEM TO EXPLORE. THEY EACH HAVE THEIR OWN IDEAS ABOUT WHAT THEY WANT TO FIND.
LOOK FOR WOOD, EVERYONE.
MAYBE WE CAN FIND MORE BONES.
MORE BONES? PACE, GIVE BACK MY TANGLE-LINE.

THERE'S NOTHING HERE ...

THE ARKIES MEET AGAIN IN THE MIDDLE OF THE ISLAND.
WHAT DO WE HAVE TO WORK WITH?
NOTHING, PACE. THE PLACE IS A DESERT.
NOTHING BUT BONES.
I'M NOT SO SURE ...

WHAT IS IT?
I DON'T KNOW ...

PACE IS WORRIED.
IF WE CAN FIND ANY SCRAPS OF WOOD I CAN CONVERT THEM INTO FOOD.
BUT WHAT IF THERE IS NO WOOD? WHAT CAN WE EAT? I'VE GOT TO THINK OF SOMETHING, FAST!

SINGER IS GAZING OUT TO SEA.
WHAT IS IT? WHAT'S WRONG WITH SINGER?
SHE'S SENSING SOMETHING.

WHAT'S OUT THERE, SINGER?
THERE'S SOMETHING IN THE WATER, PACE. I CAN SENSE IT.

SINGER REACHES OUT TO THE ALIEN MIND SHE'S DISCOVERED IN THE DEPTHS OF THE SEA.

MEANWHILE, LYAM AND MERLINNA HAVE MADE A DISCOVERY.
GUYS, LOOK AT THIS!
WE'VE FOUND SOME WATERWEED.

THAT'S NOT ALL. THE WATER'S DROPPED BACK HALF A METRE IN THE LAST MINUTE. THE TIDE MUST BE GOING OUT – AND FAST!

GREAT! LYAM, TEST THAT WATERWEED FOR TOXINS.
Ark3
HOW CAN I? ALL MY GEAR WAS WASHED AWAY.

GIVE IT TO ME! I'LL TEST IT.

Ark3

IT TASTES ALL RIGHT.
THAT STUFF COULD KILL YOU!
Ark3

SO COULD STARVATION.

PACE, LYAM AND MERLINNA GO BACK TO SINGER, WHO IS STILL TRYING TO REACH WHATEVER IS IN THE WATER.
IF THE WATER KEEPS GOING DOWN, WE CAN HEAD BACK TO WHERE WE LANDED.
WHAT FOR? ARK3 WON'T BE THERE ANY MORE.

WE'RE STRANDED ON THIS PLANET.
I'LL USE THE MATCON AND CONTACT ARKMA. SHE CAN GUIDE US TO WHEREVER SHE IS.
I HOPE.

PACE TRIES TO CONTACT ARKMA. HE FOCUSES HARD ...
C'MON, LITTLE BRO. PUT US IN TOUCH WITH ARKMA.
C'MON ... PLEASE?

WHATEVER WAS OUT THERE BEFORE IS NOW GONE.

WATERWEED, ANYONE?

PACE KEEPS TRYING TO CONTACT ARKMA.
MEANWHILE, THE OTHERS ARE BECOMING RESTLESS.

WE CAN'T WAIT ANY LONGER. LET'S GO. IF THE WATER COMES UP AGAIN, THEN WE'LL USE THE TANGLE-LINE.

WHAT ABOUT THE THINGS SINGER SENSED OUT IN THE WATER? THEY MIGHT BE DANGEROUS.
DOING NOTHING CAN BE DANGEROUS, TOO. DO YOU WANT TO END UP LIKE THOSE BONES? COME ON, PACE. WE'RE LEAVING.

WE'RE WHAT? HUH?

SORRY, LYAM, I DON'T REALLY WANT TO HANG AROUND HERE EITHER.

THE ARKIES WALK FOR HOURS. PACE IS STILL TRYING TO MAKE CONTACT WITH ARKMA.
Ark3

HEY, GUYS, LOOK AT THIS!

HUH?

IT'S JUST ANOTHER BONE. I'D BE INTERESTED IF IT HAD SOME MEAT ON IT.
THAT'S THE POINT. IT HAS. AND THAT MEANS ...

SINGER WAS RIGHT. THERE'S SOMETHING ALIVE ON THIS PLANET.

SOMETHING THAT EATS MEAT.

THE ARKIES ARE SO WORRIED ABOUT THE MEAT-EATING DIDGIES THAT THEY DON'T NOTICE THE SUN GOING DOWN - OR THE MOON GROWING EVEN LARGER IN THE SKY.
SPERLASH!

FINALLY THEY HEAR AN AWFUL, DEAFENING SOUND. IT'S THE APPROACHING TIDE.
OH-OH! THIS DOESN'T LOOK GOOD!
QUICK, PACE! HERE'S MY TANGLE-LINE. CONVERT IT AGAIN.

UH, PACE? YOU MIGHT WANT TO HURRY.

C'MON, LITTLE BRO. GIVE IT YOUR BEST SHOT.
PACE! THE CREATURE ... IT'S COMING TOWARDS US.

WHERE, SINGER?

THERE! I CAN SENSE IT!
IS IT LOOKING FOR DINNER?

I'VE FINISHED. QUICK, EVERYONE GRAB ON AND START KICKING!

THE WATER IS NOW CHEST HIGH AND THE ARKIES HAVE NO CHOICE BUT TO KICK FOR THEIR LIVES.

THERE! THERE! IT'S BEHIND US!
SWIM!
I KNEW THIS WAS A BAD IDEA. NOW WE'RE GOING TO GET EATEN!

GET AWAY, YOU BRUTE! GO!

HELP!

OH NO! IT'S GOT LYAM!

THE ARKIES TRY THEIR BEST TO ESCAPE FROM THE MONSTER, BUT THERE IS LITTLE THEY CAN DO.

I SHOULD HAVE THOUGHT OF SOMETHING.

CLUTCHING THE ARKIES IN ITS TENTACLES, THE MONSTER SWIMS SWIFTLY THROUGH THE WATERS.
ARE YOU OK?
JUST FINE, LYAM. WE'RE BEING CARRIED OFF TO THE LAIR OF A MONSTER WHERE WE'LL BE EATEN AS A SNACK. MERLINNA, DO SOMETHING!
WHAT WITH? I DON'T HAVE ANY WEAPONS EXCEPT THE TANGLE-LINE.

SINGER LINKS HANDS WITH PACE AND MERLINNA, WHO GRABS LYAM. THEY HAVE FORMED A HUMAN CHAIN AND CAN COMMUNICATE THROUGH THEIR THOUGHTS.

SINGER TRIES TO SPEAK TO THE CREATURE.

SINGER USES ALL HER SKILLS, BUT IT IS NO USE.

THE CREATURE STOPS. ITS COLOURS BRIGHTEN.
FWEEP!

PACE, IT COPIED YOU!

JUST COINCIDENCE.

NO. LOOK! IT'S CHANGED COLOUR! TRY IT AGAIN, PACE.

FWEEP!
FWEEP!

FWEEP! FWEEP!

FWEEP! FWEEP!

ALL THE ARKIES TRY TO COMMUNICATE WITH THE CREATURE.
POW! POW!
POW! POW!
DOT DOT DOT DOT. DOT. DOT DASH DOT DOT.
DOT DOT DOT DOT. DOT. DOT DASH DOT DOT.

FWEEP! FWEEP! FWEEP!
FWEEP! FWEEP! FWEEP!
DO MI SO TE RE FA LA DO.
DO MI SO TE RE FA LA DO.

IT UNDERSTANDS US!

I MEAN, IT COPIES US. BUT HOW CAN WE TELL IT WHAT W WANT TO DO?
COME TO THAT, WHAT DO WE WANT TO DO?

WE WANT TO FIND ARK3!

OF COURSE.

WHY DIDN'T I THINK OF THAT?
WE CAN'T EXPLAIN WHAT WE WANT, THOUGH.

MAYBE WE COULD STEER THE CREATURE TOWARDS ARK3.

IF WE KNEW WHERE IT WAS.

THE CREATURE SEEMS TO LIKE SINGER'S SONG.
DO MI SO TE RE FA—
WHEEEEEEEEZIZIZ

WHAT'S THAT?
OH NO ... LOOK!

chapter 5 : The Escape

OH NO, NOT AGAIN.

WHAT ARE THOSE -

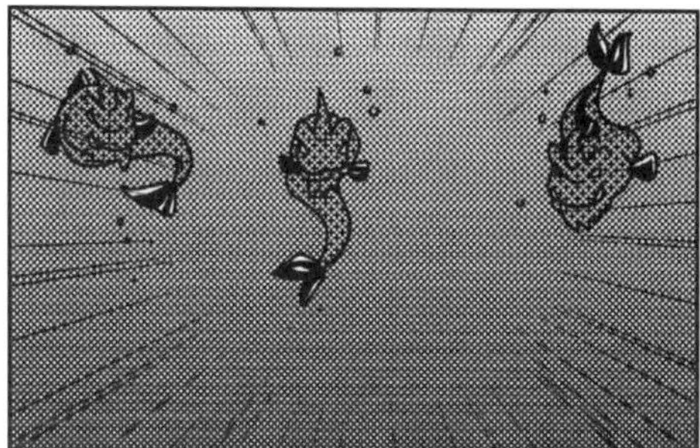

ARGHHHHHH!

THE MONSTER IS THE UGLIEST THING PACE HAS EVER SEEN.

PACE,
HELP IT!

YOU KNOW THE RULES. NO INTERFERING WITH DIDGIES. LET'S GET OUT OF HERE!
RULES ARE RULES, BUT RULES COULD GET US KILLED ...

LYAM IS RIGHT, BUT MERLINNA SOMETIMES FORGETS THE RULES.
YO! CREEPOIDS! OVER HERE!

MERLINNA, YOU IDIOT.

THE MONSTERS SEE A NEW KIND OF PREY AND CLOSE IN FOR THE KILL.

COME ON, WHO WANTS A FIGHT?

WHEEEEEEEZIZIZ

NO, MERLINNA! YOU'RE GOING TO GET US ALL KILLED!
SHE HASN'T EVEN GOT HER TANGLE-LINE.

WACK!

YAH! TAKE THAT!
WHEEEEEEEEZIZIZI

MAYBE WE CAN DISTRACT SOME OF THEM.

THE BATTLE BEGINS.
GOT YOU! DOWN!
THIS IS IMPOSSIBLE. OOOOF!
OUCH! THESE THINGS STING.

SLAP! WAM!

BAM!

THERE, THERE, NICE FISHIE!

OH NO, LYAM AND PACE ARE IN TROUBLE AND THERE ARE STILL SO MANY OF THEM ...

AIIAIIEEEEE
I WISH SHE WOULDN'T DO THAT.

AIIAIIEEEEEE

TAKE THAT, EEL MONSTERS!

GREAT, MERLINNA! YOU SAVED OUR SKINS.
AND OUR BONES! AND OUR INSIDES!

DO MI SO TE RE FA LA DO.

DO MI SO TE RE FA LA DO.
AIIAIIEEEEEEE!

GREAT. I ALWAYS THOUGHT MERLINNA HAD THE LOUDEST SCREAM IN THE GALAXY. NOW THERE ARE TWO OF THEM.

DO MI SO TE RE FA LA DO.

AIIAIIEEEEEEE!
IT CAN TELL THE DIFFERENCE BETWEEN US. I WONDER ... SINGER?
HOW DOES ARKMA SOUND WHEN SHE'S WORRIED?
E-MER-GEN-CY! E-MER-GEN-CY!
E-MER-GEN-CY! E-MER-GEN-CY!
THE CREATURE CARRIES THE ARKIES TO WHERE ARK3 HAS BEEN WASHED UP AS THE TIDE FALLS ONCE MORE.
DO MI SO TE RE FA LA DO.
GREAT! ARK3 MUST BE IN THAT DIRECTION!

E-MER-GEN-CY, E-MER-GEN-CY.

THE ARKIES ARE EXHAUSTED BUT VERY GLAD TO HAVE FOUND THEIR SHIP AGAIN.
ARKMA! WE'RE BACK!
ABOUT TIME, TOO. YOU HAVE BEEN OUT OF TOUCH MUCH TOO LONG. THIS IS NOT ACCEPTABLE. THIS IS—

WE LOVE YO
TOO, ARKMA
TIME TO LEAV
I THINK.

WITH THOSE HUGE TIDES ONLY WATER CREATURES COULD LIVE HERE.

ARK3 LIFTS OFF FROM THE PLANET OF BONES. IT HAS BEEN AN EXCITING MISSION, BUT THE PLANET IS DEFINITELY NOT S-R!

GOODBYE! REMEMBER TO SCREAM IF THOSE MONSTERS COME AFTER YOU!
DO MI SO TE RE FA LA DO. AIIAIIEEEEEEE!

ARK3 LEAVES THE PLANET BEHIND AND IS GREETED IN SPACE BY A FAMILIAR SOUND ...

DO NOT LAN
ON THAT
PLANET. DO
NOT ...

WE DIDN'T ACHIEVE MUCH THIS TIME.
BUT AT LEAST THE CREATURE CAN DEFEND ITSELF NOW.
DO NOT LAND ON THAT PLANET ...

DON'T THEY EVER GIVE UP?!
PLANET OF BONES
Official Arkie repor
NOT S-R.